KORKY THE CAT

HI, READERS! TODAY I'M A CHEF!

ER...

...CHIEF! I'M A CHIEF!

CORPORAL CLOTT

AGH! TAKE COVER! RUN FOR YOUR LIVES! IT'S CLOTT...

OH NO! HAS HE GOTTEN INTO THE ARMOURY?

HE'S NOT POLISHING THE MISSILES AGAIN, IS HE?

...HE'S ON KITCHEN DUTY!

BE HONEST, FELLAS - TOO MUCH PARSLEY?

KID COPS

IT'S A HOT DAY TO BE OUT ON POLICE PATROL, HERE IN OUR BACK GARDEN!

DO SOME CHORES FOR ME AND I'LL BUY YOU BOTH AN ICE CREAM!

SO! TRYING TO BRIBE POLICE OFFICERS, EH?

THAT'S A SERIOUS OFFENCE, MUM!

B-BUT....!

GUILTY! THE SENTENCE IS... YOU'LL BUY US ICE CREAM ANYWAY, WITHOUT US DOING THE CHORES!

SIGH! ANYTHING FOR A QUIET LIFE!

GREEDY PIGG

YOU BOYS STAY THERE! I'M OFF TO READ MY LOVELY WEIGHT-LOSS BOOKS IN PEACE!

LET'S FIND OUT WHAT HE'S REALLY UP TO!

SO, THIS IS WHY PIGGY HAS ALL THOSE DIET BOOKS!

WOBBLE! TOTTER!!

STATIONERY CUPBOARD

YEAH! HE NEEDS THEM TO REACH ALL OUR CONFISCATED GRUB!

I WONDER WHAT'LL HAPPEN IF I BORROW ONE?

TUG!

HOW TO DISLIKE CALORIES

LOVE LETTUCE!

DIET HARD

YUMMY WATER!

SHRIEK! SOMEBODY HELP ME DOWN!

HA-HA! WE'LL HELP YOU KEEP YOUR WEIGHT DOWN BY EATING ALL THESE SNACKS!

SMASHER

ZZZZ... SMASH... SMASH... SMASH... ZZZZ!

WAKE UP, SMASHER! IT'S ALRIGHT! YOU WERE HAVING A NIGHTMARE!

ZZZ... UH? WHAT?

WHEW! I WAS DREAMING I WAS A GIANT AND I WAS SMASHING UP THE CITY WITH MY BIG BOOTS, STOMPING ON ALL THE BUILDINGS!

WHAT AN AWFUL NIGHTMARE!

ARE YOU KIDDING, MUM? IT WAS A GREAT DREAM!

GULP! HE'S A STRANGE LAD SOMETIMES!

PINKY'S CRACKPOT CIRCUS

HELLO, SANTA!

SORRY, SONNY, I'M NOT SANTA. WHATEVER MADE YOU THINK THAT?

WELL, MUM SAID THAT SANTA WAS A SILLY-LOOKING FAT MAN IN A RED COAT.

BULLY BEEF AND CHIPS

HA! COME HERE, SQUIRT! I OWE YOU SUCH A BULLYING!

ER... NO YOU DON'T.

PARDON?!

ACCORDING TO MY CALCULATIONS YOU'RE ALREADY WELL AHEAD ON CHIPS-THUMPING THIS YEAR!

IN FACT, YOU DON'T NEED TO BULLY ME AGAIN UNTIL 2018! SEE?

UH?!

TIP TOE!

HEH-HEH! WHILE HE'S TRYING TO WORK THAT OUT, I'LL GO AND HIDE SOMEWHERE ELSE IN THIS ANNUAL WHERE HE CAN'T FIND ME!

DIRTY DICK

MUM HAS WRITTEN A LETTER TO MY TEACHER AND I JUST HAVE TO SEE WHAT IT SAYS.

"DEAR TEACHER, PLEASE CAN YOU EXCUSE DICK FROM ANY ACTIVITIES...

SPLOSH!

...THAT MIGHT MAKE HIM DIRTY."

SECRET AGENT SALLY

BURIED DEEP IN THE NORTHERN ICE FLOWS OF THE NORTH POLE, SALLY AND GUS MAKE THEIR WAY TO ARCTIC SCIENCE STATION VII IN ANSWER TO A DISTRESS SIGNAL THAT WAS PICKED UP TWO DAYS AGO...

HURRY UP, GUS.

MAN, THIS IS COLD...

IT'S THE NORTH POLE, GUS. IT TENDS TO GET A LITTLE NIPPY FROM TIME TO TIME.

OH HAR-HAR... VERY FUNNY. YOU KNOW WHAT I MEAN.

WHY ARE YOU TAKING YOUR COAT OFF? AREN'T YOU COLD?

NO. IT'S A SPECIAL ISSUE SUPER THERMAL, LIGHT-WEIGHT SUIT THAT FAIRFAX CREATED FOR US BOTH.

DO YOU MEAN TO SAY THERE'S A SPECIAL SUIT FOR ME BACK...

...WHOA, WHAT HAPPENED HERE?!

SOMEONE SURE DID A NUMBER ON THIS PLACE.

LOOK, I'VE FOUND A COMPANY LAPTOP UNTOUCHED AND THERE APPEARS TO BE A MESSAGE.

PEPPERONI PIG!

A RED-RIDING VESPA-PIGGY!

THIS IS PEPPERONI PIG. HER JOB IS TO DELIVER PIZZAS.

THIS IS BIG BAD WOLF. HE WANTS TO **EAT** PEPPERONI PIG.

THIS IS A HOLE IN THE ROAD WITH SPIKES IN IT. WHICH SEEMS A LITTLE DANGEROUS!

THIS IS A TRAP – A TRAP FOR PEPPERONI PIG!

THIS IS... AWFUL! POOR PEPPERONI PIG IS GOING TO BE...
...OH, I CAN'T LOOK!

THIS IS... ODD!

THIS IS NOT WHAT BIG BAD WOLF EXPECTED TO HAPPEN!

THIS IS BIG BAD WOLF TESTING HIS TRAP.
THIS IS **NOT** A GOOD IDEA!

THIS IS KARMA!*
*LOOK IT UP IN THE DICTIONARY!

THIS IS PEPPERONI, ON HER WAY BACK FROM DELIVERING THE PIZZA.

THIS IS VERY NICE OF PEPPERONI PIG. LET'S HOPE BIG BAD WOLF REMEMBERS IT!

BERYL THE PERIL

BERYL! WHAT ARE YOU DOING?

PRACTISING MY SKATEBOARDING!

YOU NEED SOME NEW HOBBIES! HERE, READ THIS!

'THE BIG BOOK OF HOBBIES FOR NICE GIRLS'? SIGH. IF YOU SAY SO, DAD.

SOON...

I'LL TRY THIS ONE. POTTERY.

A NEW PUPIL! SOON YOU'LL BE MAKING PRIZE VASES, LIKE THESE!

FIRST STEP – SPIN THE CLAY ON YOUR WHEEL.

I NEED TO GET THIS MOVING IF I'M GOING TO MAKE A GREAT POT!

WHIZZ!

PUMP! PUMP!

PUMP! PUMP!

WHOOPS! TOO FAST!

WHOOSH!

CRASH!

THE VASES!

BETTER TRY ANOTHER HOBBY.

OH, THIS LOOKS COOL. PONY TREKKING!

AND SO...

NEARLY READY TO GO! WE'RE JUST WAITING FOR ONE MORE GIRL.

POSTMAN PRAT

BAH! A BAG FULL OF POST TO DELIVER! HAVEN'T THESE PEOPLE HEARD OF EMAIL?

I WANT TO BE FINISHED BEFORE LUNCH! I'M GOING TO DELIVER THIS POST SUPER FAST!

HEY! THIS LETTER'S FOR NUMBER 54! THIS IS NUMBER 56!

AND THIS LETTER'S FOR NUMBER 21! THIS IS NUMBER 58!

JUST TWO TINY MISTAKES!

UH-OH!

THIS IS THE RIGHT NUMBER BUT THE WRONG STREET!

YOU'VE POSTED A CARD TELLING ME YOU'RE SORRY I'M OUT! I'VE JUST CHECKED THE MIRROR AND I'M IN!

FOR SOME REASON YOU'VE POSTED ME YOUR CAP!

I THOUGHT MY HEAD WAS COLD!

WHAT IS IT YOU WANT?

OUR POST!

MUCH LATER...

WHAT A DAY! PEOPLE DON'T REALISE HOW HARD IT IS BEING A POSTMAN!

EH? WHAT ARE YOU DOING IN MY HOUSE AND WHY HAVE YOU REDECORATED?

THIS IS OUR HOUSE! YOU LIVE IN THE NEXT STREET!

HE CAN'T EVEN DELIVER HIMSELF TO THE RIGHT ADDRESS!

SCRIPT: D. MASON / ART: L. STRINGER

KORKY THE CAT

CORPORAL CLOTT

KID COPS

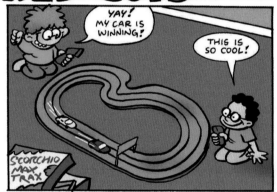

GREEDY PIGG

SMASHER

OOPS! SORRY, DAD!

BAH! NOT AGAIN!

I'VE BOUGHT YOU A FOAM BALL! THERE'S NO DANGER OF YOU SMASHING ANOTHER WINDOW IN MY GREENHOUSE!

HUH!

OOPS! MAYBE YOU SHOULD HAVE BOUGHT ME FOAM SHOES INSTEAD, DAD!

NYAAGH!

LEW STRINGER

PINKY'S CRACKPOT CIRCUS

MERRY CHRISTMAS! YOU SAID YOU ALWAYS WANTED A BIKE!

HIGH WIRE

I DID! I'LL TAKE IT FOR A RIDE!

PRANCE!

JUST A PAIR OF SLIPPERS WILL DO NEXT YEAR!

WOBBLE!

NICK BRENNAN

BULLY BEEF AND CHIPS

HA! BULLY BEEF'S MUM HAS CONFISCATED HIS WEIGHTS!

WHIMPER! I CAN FEEL MY MUSCLES WASTING AWAY ALREADY!

IF I PLAY THE WEIGHTING GAME, HE'LL BE SCRAWNY LIKE ME IN NO TIME!

AHA! YOU'LL DO!

OH DEAR. WHAT DO YOU MEAN?!

I KNEW I SHOULDN'T HAVE WEIGHTED WHERE HE COULD SEE ME!

HUP! HUP! HUP!

AND JUST YOU WEIGHT UNTIL I GET MY STRENGTH BACK, SQUIRT!

DIRTY DICK

I'M HELPING MUM CLEAN BY HOOVERING THE CARPET.

AND THE CURTAINS.

BEHIND THE SIDEBOARD.

AND...

...MYSELF! SIGH.

BERYL THE PERIL

A PET SHOW? I COULD EASILY WIN THAT! THE ONLY THING IS, I DON'T HAVE A PET!

WELL, NOT YET!

DANDYTOWN PET SHOW!

AMAZING PRIZES!

HI, DAD! CAN I HAVE A PET?

NO.

WHAT? THAT'S SO UNFAIR! WHY NOT?

YOU'D NEVER LOOK AFTER IT.

STAMP!

LATER...

I'LL SHOW HIM! AH, IS THIS PETS FOR CRAZY PEOPLE?

I HOPE BERYL HAS FORGOTTEN ALL ABOUT THAT PET SHE WANTED.

ARGH!

HI, DAD. I SEE YOU FOUND CRUSHER! I THOUGHT I'D LOST HIM!

BERYL! I CAN'T BREATHE!

SSSILLY MAN! I'M JUST GIVING YOU A HUG!

DON'T WORRY. ALL YOU HAVE TO DO IS TICKLE HIM AND HE LETS GO - SEE?

TEE-HEE-HEE! I LOVE A TICKLE ON THE TAIL!

YES, I'D LIKE TO SPEAK TO SOMEONE IN PEST CONTROL, PLEASE.

OUT! AND DON'T EVER SLITHER INTO THIS HOUSE AGAIN!

CRUMBS! YOU REALLY UPSET HIM!

THE END!

agent dog 2 zero

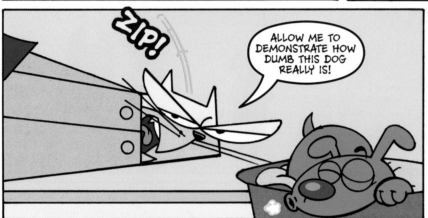

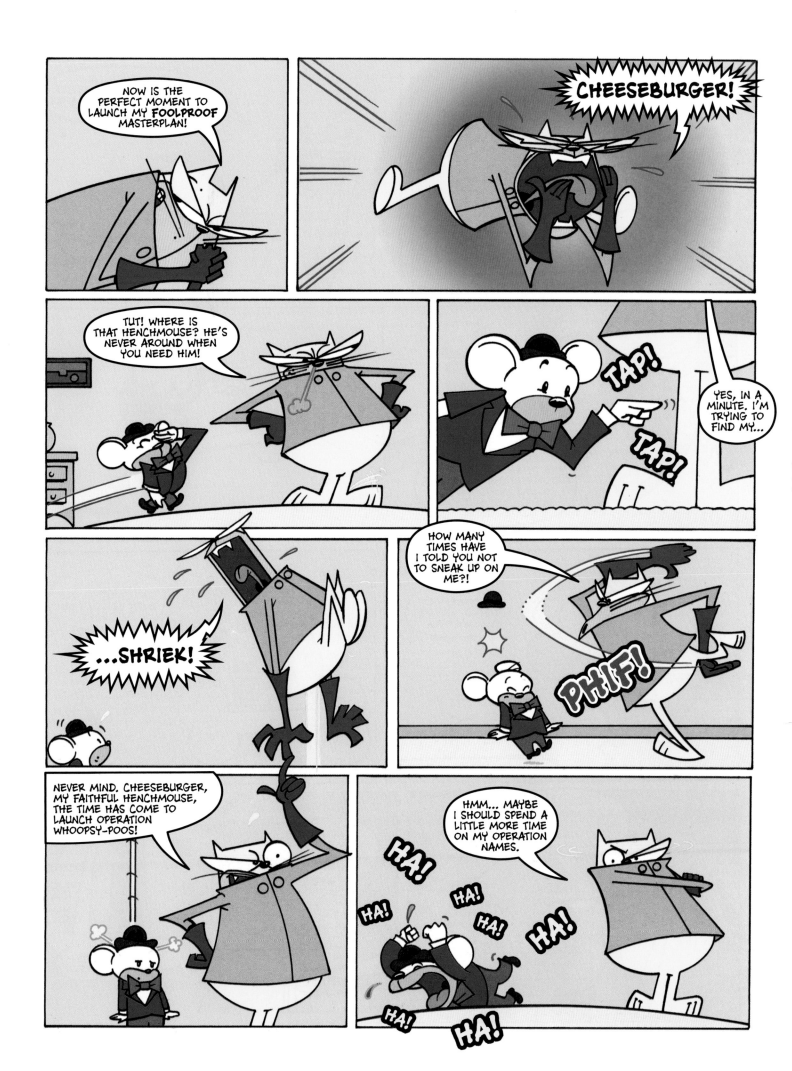

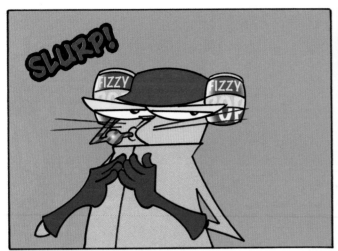

SLURP!

ZERO? CAN YOU HEAR ME, ZERO?

I.... HEAR YOU... MASTER!

YOU MUST WEE ON MASTER'S BEST SLIPPERS!

YES, MASTER!

MUST... FIND... MASTER! MUST... WEE ON HIM!

TARGET ACQUIRED, MASTER!

HE'S DOING IT! HE'S DOING IT!

WHAT IS IT? WHY DON'T YOU WEE ON HIS FOOT, YOU SILLY DOG?!

PAUSED!

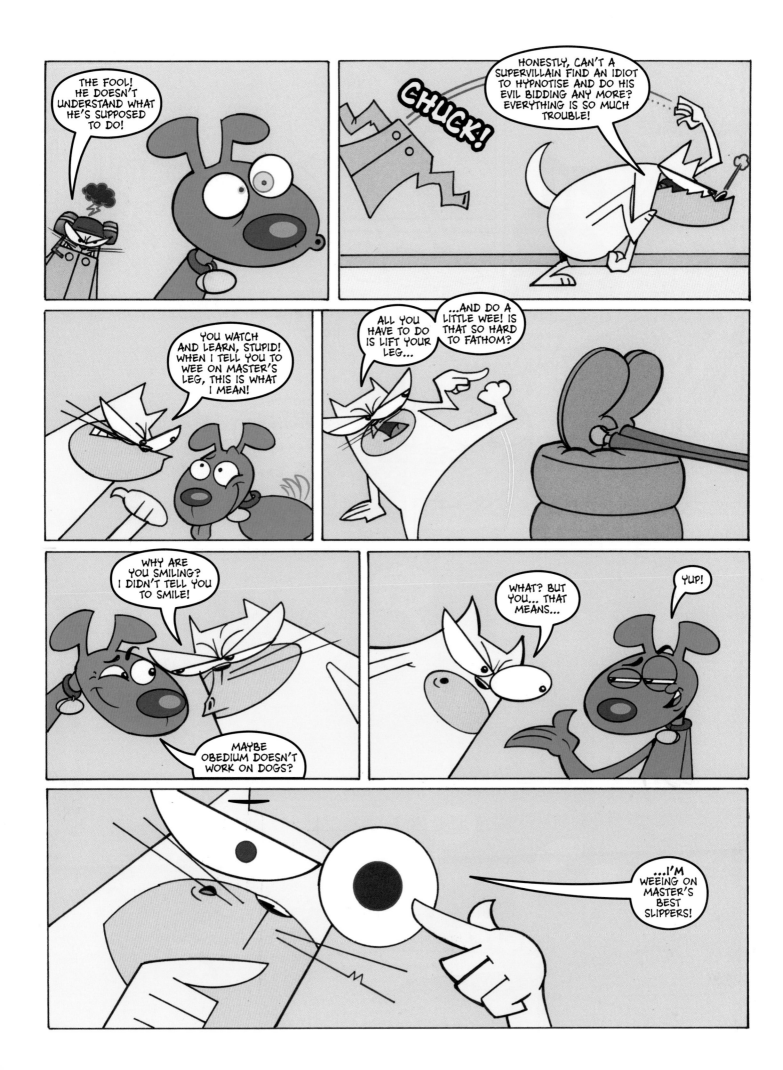

PEPPERONI PIG!

WE ARE THE HAM-PIONS, MY FRIENDS...

SUDDENLY...

A-HA! MY DINNER HAS ARRIVED JUST IN TIME! I'M SOOO HUNGRY I COULD EAT A PIG!

EEK!

WOULDN'T YOU RATHER HAVE A YUMMY PIZZA BALL INSTEAD?

I DON'T KNOW. WHAT'S A PIZZA BALL?

THEY'RE PIZZAS BEFORE THEY GET FLAT.

REALLY? GET OUTTA HERE!

BUT HOW DO YOU GET THEM FLAT?

IT'S A SECRET! I CAN'T TELL YOU!

PLEASE, TELL ME THE SECRET! PLEASE! PLEASE!

OKAY - BUT YOU HAVE TO CLOSE YOUR EYES!

I WON'T! I WON'T!

AND NO PEEKING!

BLAM!

THAT'S HOW WE GET 'EM FLAT!

PIZZA CAKE, ISN'T IT?

GROAN!

TO BE CONTINUED!

TODAY'S SPECIAL:
MY DAD'S A DOOFUS
+CHIPS

BLUGHH! LUNCH IN THE SCHOOL CANTEEN IS DISGUSTING! WHAT EVEN IS THIS SLOP?

RAISIN SLOP.

RAISIN SLOP! BLUGH!

SLOP!

HANG ON, I JUST REMEMBERED I'M A GROWN-UP!

I CAN DO WHAT I LIKE!

WHERE ARE YOU GOING?

TWO MONSTER WHOPPING BURGERS PLEASE, WITH TRIPLE FRIES AND A STRAWBERRY SLODGESHAKE EACH!

BURGERS

ONE OF THE BEST THINGS ABOUT BEING A GROWN-UP IS EATING JUNK FOOD IN YOUR CAR.

THIS WAS A GREAT IDEA!

A WEEK LATER...

WHEEZE! WE MAY HAVE TO STOP DOING THIS, SON. I THINK I MAY BE PUTTING ON WEIGHT.

DAD, IS THE CAR MOVING?

ARGH! WE'RE SO HEAVY, WE'RE ROLLING THE CAR FORWARD!

STEER, DAD! STEER!!

I CAN'T! I CAN'T REACH THE WHEEL!

SMASH!!

HOSPITAL

WHAT'S FOR LUNCH TODAY, NURSE?

SAME AS EVERY DAY... RAISIN SLOP!

BLUGHHHH!

KORKY THE CAT

HI, READERS! TODAY I'M A PLUMBER!

WAH!

CORPORAL CLOTT

AH... PEACE AT LAST. CLOTT IS TAKING THE MEN FOR DRILL PRACTICE THIS MORNING.

DRRRRRRRR

AAAAGH! EARTHQUAKE! TAKE THEM! I'M TOO YOUNG TO DIE!

BUT...

CLOTT! I SAID DRILL PRACTICE, YOU IDIOT, NOT DRILL PRACTICE!

DRRRRRRR

KID COPS

WE'VE BEEN QUESTIONING YOU FOR HOURS NOW!

YEAH! WE'RE NOT GIVING IN UNTIL YOU CONFESS!

COME ON! ADMIT IT! YOU DID IT, DIDN'T YOU?

OKAY, I CONFESS! IT WAS ME!

RESULT! I KNEW IT!

IT WAS THE SPROUTS! THE SPROUTS MADE ME DO IT!

GREEDY PIGG

BRRIIINNGG!

RUN FOR IT, LADS! PIGGY'S TAKING OUR ART LESSON!

I KNOW. PUFF! PANT!

BUT WHY THE RUSH?

WE'RE PAINTING A STILL LIFE TODAY! IF WE DON'T GET THERE EARLY ENOUGH...

CHOMP! MUNCH! CHEW!

...PIGGY WILL HAVE EATEN OUR LESSON!

TOO LATE, BOYS. YOU SNOOZE, YOU LOSE! I DON'T KNOW MUCH ABOUT ART BUT I KNOW WHAT I LIKE! BURP!

SMASHER

BEHAVE YOURSELF TODAY, SMASHER!

COMFY'S SOFT FURNISHINGS

CUSHIONS
SHEETS
DUVETS
IF IT'S SOFT WE SELL IT.

SALE

RELAX, DAD! AT LEAST HE CAN'T SMASH ANYTHING IN A SOFT FURNISHING STORE!

PILLOW FIGHT!

OOPS!

SLIP!

WHUMP!

STORE MANAGER

SIGH! HE'S SMASHED THE RECORD OF GETTING BANNED FROM A SHOP IN TEN SECONDS!

COMFY'S SOFT FURNISHINGS

LEW STRINGER

PINKY'S CRACKPOT CIRCUS

I'VE...

...BROUGHT ME A CHRISTMAS PRESENT.

JACK BRENNAN

IT'S...

...A PRETTY BLUE DRESS.

I DON'T KNOW HOW MADAME GRIZELDA ALWAYS KNOWS WHAT I'VE BOUGHT HER.

FORTUNES TOLD

SEE TOMORROW TODAY!

I SEE THE FUTURE

BULLY BEEF AND CHIPS

GRR! C'MERE, SQUIRT! IT'S TIME TO THUMP YOU INTO NEXT YEAR'S ANNUAL!

CUT!

UH? CUT?! WHAT DO YOU MEAN... CUT?!

DIDN'T I TELL YOU? I'VE HIRED A STUNT DOUBLE!

B-BUT HE LOOKS NOTHING LIKE YOU!

DON'T WORRY, BEEFY! NOBODY WILL NOTICE! AND... ACTION!

ER, C'MERE... SQUIRT?

WHIMPER! SOB!!

HA-HA! ANY NERVOUS READERS WHO DON'T LIKE VIOLENCE SHOULD LOOK AWAY NOW!

DIRTY DICK

I'M GOING TO POLE VAULT OVER THIS PUDDLE...

...TO MAKE SURE I DON'T GET DIRTY!

OOPS! LOOKS LIKE I'VE VAULTED TOO FAR!

RIGHT INTO THE TOWN DUMP!

BRASSNECK!

BRASSNECK AND CHARLEY ARE IN THE MIDDLE OF A HISTORY TEST AND QUESTION FOUR IS VERY TRICKY...

WHO WON THE BATTLE OF ZORNDORF IN 1758?

PSST! BRASSNECK! YOU'RE A ROBOT! GO ON THE INTERNET IN YOUR HEAD AND FIND OUT WHO WON THE BATTLE OF ZORNDORF.

GOOD IDEA!

SEARCHING!

OKAY, WRITE THIS DOWN. IT SAYS, "THIS PAGE CANNOT BE OPENED BECAUSE YOU ARE NOT CONNECTED TO THE INTERNET."

COOL, THANKS! "THIS... PAGE... CANNOT... BE..."

...WAIT A MINUTE! THAT'S NOT THE ANSWER! YOUR INTERNET IS DOWN!

OH!

I KNOW. THE ANSWERS ARE ON THE TEACHER'S DESK. I'LL DETACH MY HAND AND STICK MY EYE TO IT...

...THERE! OKAY, LITTLE GUY, GO SEE WHAT THE ANSWER TO QUESTION FOUR IS.

SURE THING, BOSS!

BRASSNECK'S TINY SECRET AGENT CLIMBS UP ONTO THE TEACHER'S DESK...

...AND HAS A PEEK AT THE ANSWERS!

THE RESULT WAS...

...INCONCLUSIVE?!

NO ONE REALLY WON. IT WAS SORT OF A DRAW! – ED.

PRAT, THERE'S QUITE A LOT OF MAIL TODAY! IT'S THE RUN UP TO CHRISTMAS SO THERE ARE SACKFULLS OF CHRISTMAS CARDS TO DELIVER!

NO PROBLEM, BOSS! I KNOW YOU ALWAYS TAKE ON EXTRA PEOPLE AT CHRISTMAS TO HELP DELIVER THEM!

NOT THIS YEAR! TOO MANY CUTBACKS! YOU'RE ON YOUR OWN! NOW DELIVER THIS LOT!

AWK!

I'LL NEVER HAVE TIME TO DELIVER THIS LOT ON MY OWN! WHAT CAN I DO?

I KNOW! I'LL SUB-CONTRACT! I'LL EMPLOY MY OWN WORKFORCE TO HELP OUT!

HANG ON THOUGH. IF I PAY PEOPLE TO HELP ME, I'LL BE OUT OF POCKET! HMM...

I KNOW! I'LL PAY THEM IN MINCE PIES! EVERYONE LIKES MINCE PIES AT CHRISTMAS!

LATER...

OKAY, I SUPPOSE IF YOU PAY PEANUTS YOU GET MONKEYS AND IF YOU PAY MINCE PIES YOU GET YOU LOT, BUT WE'LL MAKE THE BEST OF IT!

HOME MADE MINCE PIES

DROOL! CAN I HAVE MY PAYMENT IN ADVANCE, PLEASE, PRAT?

OH GO ON THEN. JUST ONE!

SCOFF!

YERK! I MEANT ONE PIE, NOT ONE PLATEFUL!

URRRGH! THOSE PIES WERE OFF, - AND SO AM I NOW!

GENTS

RRUMBLE!

BLOIK!

BAH! NOW WE'RE ONE MAN DOWN!

WHERE'S OUR INCENTIVE TO WORK NOW THE PIES ARE GONE?

ERM... FOR THE GOOD OF THE COMMUNITY? IT IS CHRISTMAS, AFTER ALL!

GRUMBLE! ALRIGHT THEN.

GOOD MAN! NOW GET THIS PARCEL DELIVERED!

YIPES!

OOF! GOT ANYTHING LIGHTER?

Winker WATSON

It's a cold day in December, and there's a chill in the air at Greytowers School...

The showers are cold!

It's an outrage!

What?!

I don't like this at all!

Come back here, stupid mouse!

Mr Creep, Sir – the showers were freezing this morning.

Could you mention it to the caretaker?

Cold showers are good for you, Watson! We teachers didn't become the men we are today by having lovely hot showers!

Now where did that wretched mouse go?

More like the school's decided to save a bit of money heating our water!

The absolute bounders!

Don't worry, lads, I'll think of something.

Oh, we know, Winker.

We're *not* worried in the least!

I thought as much! The boiler in the teachers' part of the building is on! *They're* not having cold showers!

ON ↕ OFF

The utter rotters!

The sports hall is in this part of the building, too, Trotty, so we can all have a nice hot bath, just like after footy matches!

SPLOSH

Come on, chaps, the coast's clear.

We've got a good hour for a nice soak while the teachers have their staff meeting.

Once again, we bathe in Winker's glory!

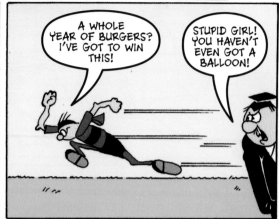

BERYL THE PERIL

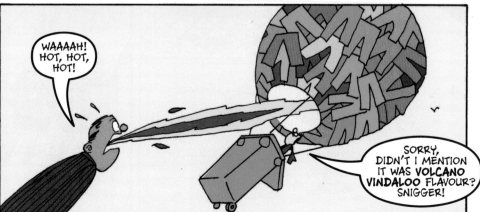

BLINKY

IS THAT A LETTER TO SANTA, SON?

NOBODY WRITES LETTERS ANY MORE, MOTHER! IT'S AN EMAIL.

AN EMAIL OF COMPLAINT!

HE ALWAYS BRINGS ME RUBBISH PRESENTS.

LAST YEAR HE BROUGHT ME A BROKEN YO-YO...

...A BELT THAT WAS WAAAAAAAY TOO SMALL...

...AND THE CHOCOLATES WERE HORRIBLE!

NOW POP MY EMAIL IN THE COMPUTER...

...AND IT'S ON ITS WAY TO SANTA. THAT'LL TELL HIM!

AND IT'S TOLD US THAT YOU'RE BONKERS!

PEPPERONI PIG!

A RED-PIZZA-LOVING-PIGGY!

HELLO, WAR 'N' PIZZA! CAN I TAKE YOUR ORDER PLEASE?

A PIZZA WITH NO TOPPING? ARE YOU SURE? OKAY! BYE!

BRING! BRING!

I'VE NEVER HEARD OF A PIZZA WITH NO TOPPING!

SLURP! I CAN'T WAIT TILL MY PIZZA ARRIVES! I'M STARVING!

HERE YOU GO, BIG BAD WOLF - BUT I DOUBT A PIZZA WITH NO TOPPING WILL BE VERY TASTY!

BUT, PEPPERONI, DON'T YOU SEE...

...YOU'RE ARE THE TOPPING!

EEK!

I DIDN'T KNOW PIGS COULD CLIMB TREES! - ED

I'M NOT A PIG, REMEMBER - I'M A PIZZA TOPPING!

SCARPER!

I DIDN'T THINK THEY COULD CLIMB TREES EITHER! - ARTIST

YOU KNOW, I THINK YOU'RE RIGHT... WE CAN'T!

PLUMMET!

BLAM!

GROAN! NOW I'M THE TOPPING ON MY OWN PIZZA!

LUCKY YOU WERE STANDING THERE! WHAT A PIZZA LUCK!

BRASSNECK!

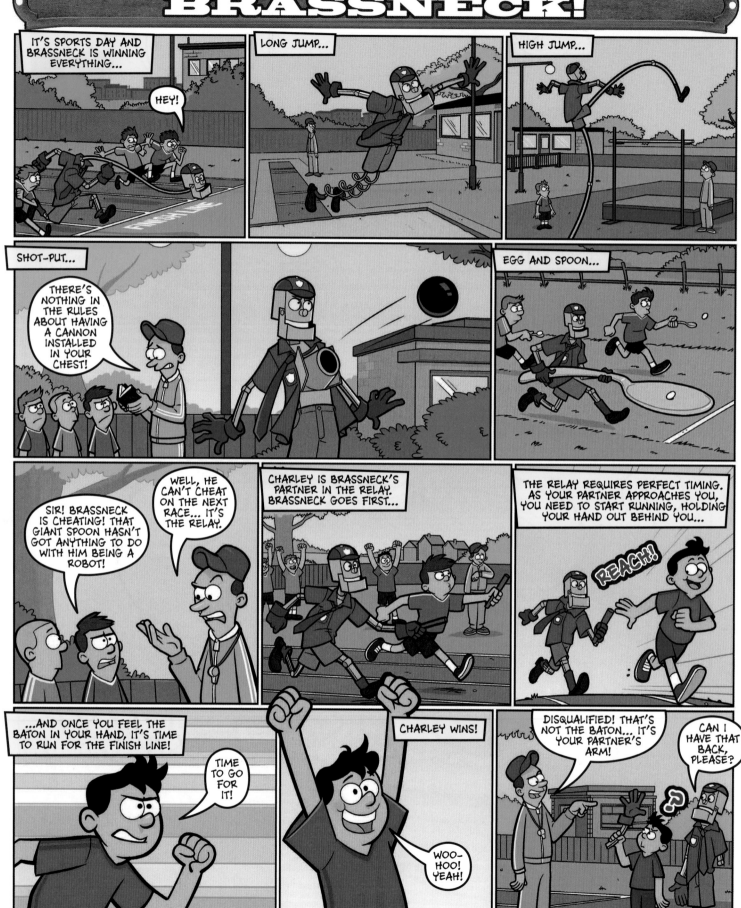

KORKY THE CAT

HI, READERS! TODAY I'M A DOG WALKER!

GRRRRR!!!

WAIT A MINUTE... AREN'T I A CAT?!

ARRRGH!!!

CORPORAL CLOTT

HULLO, LADS. I FOUND THIS THING OVER BY THE ARMOURY – WHAT DO YOU RECKON IT IS?

IT'S A MINE!

IT'S A – YOURS?

NO! NOT MINE! A MINE!

IT'S A MINE, CLOTT!

NO NEED TO FIGHT OVER IT, LADS! HERE, TAKE IT AND SORT IT OUT YOURSELVES!

TOSS!

NOOO!

THUD! CLICK!

OHHHH... A MINE!

AR!

KID COPS

HERE'S THOSE TWO KIDS WHO ALWAYS DRESS UP AS POLICEMEN! LET'S HAVE A BIT OF FUN WITH THEM!

HOLD IT RIGHT THERE, KIDS! DO YOU KNOW IT'S A SERIOUS OFFENCE TO IMPERSONATE POLICE OFFICERS?

YES, WE KNOW, AND WE FIND YOU GUILTY!

TAKE THEM AWAY, BOYS!

B-BUT... WE'RE THE REAL COPS!

NICE TRY! YOU'RE NICKED!

GREEDY PIGG

PIRATES USED TREASURE MAPS TO HELP THEM REMEMBER WHERE THEY HID THEIR BOOTY!

MAP MAKING!

BURIED FOOD!

HEH-HEH! THIS MAP WILL KEEP OUR GRUB HIDDEN FROM PIGGY!

OH NO, IT WON'T!

BURIED FOOD

YARRRR! PIECES OF CAKE! THE BOOTY BE MINE! ALL MINE!

HA-HA! PIGGY FELL FOR OUR FAKE TREASURE MAP!

AND WE'LL HAVE FINISHED OFF OUR BOOTY BY THE TIME HE REALISES!

CHOMP! CHEW!!

GRRR! WHERE IS IT?!

SMASHER

PINKY'S CRACKPOT CIRCUS

BULLY BEEF AND CHIPS

DIRTY DICK

NIGEL PARKINSON.

WE NEED TO GET THE COMPUTER TO MR DELUC IMMEDIATELY.

LOOK OUT AHEAD! INCOMING!

HEADS-UP, BOYS!

THOK!

DOOF!

OOF!

UGG!

GUS! YOU DEAL WITH THOSE TWO, I'LL TAKE OUT CHUCKLES!

MY PLEASURE! HERE I COME, BOYS, READY OR NOT!

MEET MY BIG FOOT!

TCHAK!

DUFF!

SHOVE!

ROAR!

HE'S TOO STRONG! I NEED A LITTLE BACK UP OVER HERE!

SOME ANSWERS LATER...

TO BE CONTINUED...

AND OUR *FIRST* COUPLE ARE *DESPERATE DAN,* AND HIS PARTNER, *OLGA TOPPLEOVA!*

HELLO MUM

WHAT *HAPPENED?*

HE TROD ON MY *FEET!* HE TROD ON MY *FINGERS!* HE TROD ALL *OVER* ME! I AM BROKEN TO *BITS!*

DOCTOR KEVF

ER, *LISTEN,* DAN. WE'VE GOT TWO MINUTES TO *FILL.* CAN'T YOU *FLING* HER *AROUND* A BIT?

NOT WHAT I MEANT!

I THINK SHE'LL LAND *SEV-EN* MILES AWAY!

C'MON, *AUNT AGGIE,* PLEASE DANCE WITH ME!

DANIEL! I'M 97!

BUT WHAT CAN I *DO?* I SIMPLY *MUST* WIN *STRICTLY!*

WHO'S *STRONG* ENOUGH TO *DANCE* WITH ME?

NEXT UP, IT'S *CORPORAL CLOTT* AND HIS PARTNER...

...HUH?

MY MUM!!

COO-EE, SWEETIE.

URGH! *NO!* STOP *LOOKING!* YOU'RE *EMBARRASSING* ME, MOTHER!

YOU'RE THE *CLOTTED CREME* DE LA CREME, DARLING!

MY *FAVOURITE!*

CRINGE. SO *HUMILIATING.* #TELLMEWHENITSOVER

OUR NEXT CONTESTANT IS *BRASSNECK,* WHO WILL BE DANCING *WITH...*

SHAKE RATTLE

...BRASSNECK! STOP! *THAT'S* NOT YOUR DANCING PARTNER!

THAT'S THE CAMERA!

BUT SHE IS *SO* *BLEEP* PRETTY!

BLEEP! CAN I JUST LEAVE HER MY MOBILE NUMBER?

YES, YES, DON'T CALL *US*...

NOW *THIS* IS MORE LIKE IT! *BULLY BEEF* WITH HIS PARTNER - *CHIPS!*

THWMP!

WHOOSH!

THUD!

HOW MANY OUT OF TEN DID YOU *SAY...?*

NOW THE *JOCKS* AND THEIR PARTNERS, THE *GEORDIES!*

WHY *AYE,* PET!

WHAT *DANCE* WILL YOU BE DOING?

YE KEN THE *NICHT* WE'LL BE DAEIN' A *FOXTROT!*

WHO MENTIONED *FOXES* IN FRONT OF *KORKY?*

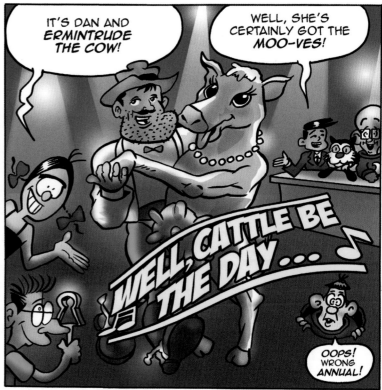

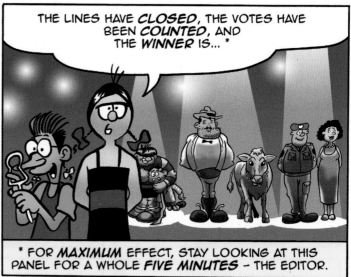

BRASSNECK!

IT'S HISTORY AGAIN AND TEACHER IS ASKING SOME TRICKY QUESTIONS...

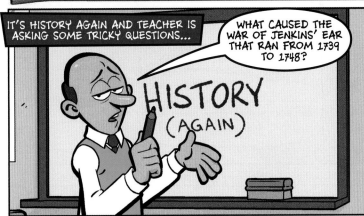

WHAT CAUSED THE WAR OF JENKINS' EAR THAT RAN FROM 1739 TO 1748?

COME ON! THERE'S A CLUE IN THE NAME!

IT WAS FOUGHT BETWEEN BRITAIN AND SPAIN!

YOU SHOULD KNOW THIS! WAR OF JENKINS' EAR? 1739? **CAPTAIN** JENKINS? ANYONE? ANYONE?

WE'RE IN TROUBLE HERE, BRASSNECK. IF NO-ONE PUTS THEIR HAND UP, HE MIGHT ASK US!

DON'T WORRY, I HAVE A PLAN!

AH, YES! MARCUS!

WHAT? ER... I... ER...

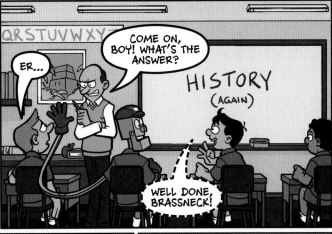

ER...

COME ON, BOY! WHAT'S THE ANSWER?

WELL DONE, BRASSNECK!

URRGH! OKAY! THE WAR OF JENKINS' EAR STARTED BECAUSE THE ENGLISH CAPTAIN, ROBERT JENKINS WAS CAPTURED BY THE SPANISH WHO THOUGHT HE WAS A PIRATE AND CUT HIS EAR OFF, WHICH WAS A THING THEY DID TO PIRATES BACK THEN.

NEXT QUESTION, WHO WON THE THIRD PUNIC WAR THAT RAN FROM 149 TO 146 BC?

YES, CHARLEY?

OI!

Winker WATSON

The mighty wangler Winker Watson and his Greytower pals are on their way to a football match against Stonelands School.

Can we have the radio on, please, Mr Creep?

No we may not. You should see this journey as an opportunity for quiet study.

Aw, Sir!

Soon the match is under way, with a Stonelands teacher refereeing.

No goal! You pushed our boy, there, number 7.

Free-kick to Stonelands.

Their ref's biased beyond belief!

Complete blighter!

The dodgy refereeing only gets worse as the first half goes on...

A penalty !?

I didn't touch him!

PHEEEP!

DIVE

It's just not cricket!

You're right there.

GOAL!

Winker, you've got to d...

I know, Trotty, I know...

Thanks to the ref, at half-time it's 2-0 to Stonelands. Thanks to Winker, Greytowers might have a better chance in the 2nd half.

Oops! Careful, Trotty!

Nudge!

Sorry, Sir.

Good work, Trotty. A bit of this in the ref's tea should help get us - and him - unstuck!

Hee-hee!

OLD MIGGINS' PATENTED Constipation POWDER

Sure enough, early in the second half...

Er, sorry, I'm going to have to leave the field on a rather urgent matter...

...Mr Creep, you'll have to take over the refereeing.

PARP!

Oh, er, right-o!

With Creep refereeing fairly, Greytowers get back in the game.

Terrific ball, Winker!

PAF

MY DAD'S A DOOFUS

CAN ANYONE TELL ME WHEN THE DINOSAURS DIED OUT?

TY'S DAD PROBABLY CAN, SIR.

HE WAS THERE AT THE TIME!

HOW DARE YOU! I'M NO OLDER THAN THE REST OF YOU!

WELL, TECHNICALLY YOU **ARE**, DAD.

EVERYONE MEET ME OUTSIDE IN FIVE MINUTES AND I'LL **SHOW** YOU HOW OLD I AM!

UHH...I'M STILL TEACHING CLASS...

FIVE MINUTES!

FIVE MINUTES LATER...

RIGHT, WELL, AS IT HAPPENS I'VE JUST STARTED DOING **PARKOUR**.

LOOK AT ME PARKOURING LIKE A YOUNG PERSON!

PARKOUR!

PARKOUR!

ARGH! A BIN!

CLATTER!

GASP! I KNOW YOUR DAD!

THE 'OLD MAN CAN'T DO **PARKOUR**' VIDEO WENT VIRAL LAST WEEK!

STOP FILMING ME!

YOUR DAD'S A **LEGEND**!!

SNIFF! THIS IS MY PROUDEST MOMENT.

IF THIS IS WHAT BEING OLD IS LIKE...

...THEN I'M DONE WITH BEING YOUNG!

NEXT WEEK, I'LL TEACH YOU TO MAKE NOISES WHEN YOU SIT DOWN.

PEPPERONI PIG!

KORKY THE CAT

CORPORAL CLOTT

KID COPS

GREEDY PIGG

SMASHER

EVERY TIME!

SORRY, SIR!

WELL, IT'S SWIMMING TODAY! AT LEAST YOU CAN'T SMASH ANYTHING IN THE WATER! HA-HA!

GAH! THEY SHOULD RE-NAME YOU SPLASHER!

SPLASH!

PINKY'S CRAZY CIRCUS

A FEW HOURS ON THE TRAMPOLINE WILL BURN OFF THAT PLUM DUFF!

CIRCUS EXERCISE PLAN

BOING!

SOON HAVE YOU ALL IN SHAPE!

THEY GOT YOU INTO THE SHAPE OF A PANCAKE.

SPLAT!

BULLY BEEF AND CHIPS

BOOK SHOP

I'VE HAD ENOUGH OF BEEFY'S BULLYING! I NEED TO LEARN SELF-DEFENCE!

BLIMEY! THIS BOOK IS HEAVY!

THE ART OF SELF-DEFENCE VOL 1

HA-HA! HILARIOUS! SO I CAN BULLY YOU PROPERLY FOR BEING SUCH A PATHETIC WIMP!

OKAY!

DROP!

ARGH! MY POOR TOES!

GRR! JUST YOU WAIT UNTIL I'VE STOPPED HOPPING, SQUIRT!

HA-HA! I'D BEST GET VOLUME TWO SHARPISH THEN!

HOP! HOP!!

DIRTY DICK

CAN YOU PROMISE ME YOU'LL KEEP YOURSELF CLEAN TODAY, DICK?

I PROMISE, DAD!

LATER...

DICK! YOU'RE A TOTAL MESS. YOU PROMISED ME!

I KNOW, BUT OBVIOUSLY MY CLOTHES DIDN'T!

BERYL THE PERIL

BAD GRANDAD

THE END... FOR NOW!

BERYL THE PERIL

TURN THAT OFF, BERYL! YOU CAN'T SPEND **ALL** YOUR TIME WATCHING TV!

AWW! I WAS WATCHING AN ACE PROGRAMME ABOUT **BREAKING WORLD RECORDS!**

I KNOW! I'M **GREAT** AT BREAKING THINGS! I'LL BREAK MY **OWN** RECORDS!

GULP! IF YOU NEED ME, I'LL BE ON A WORLD CRUISE!

NOW, LET ME THINK. WORLD'S BIGGEST CATAPULT? NAH, DID THAT YESTERDAY. WORLD'S BIGGEST PEASHOOTER? THAT WAS LAST WEEK.

I KNOW!

THAT'S SNOBBINGTON CASTLE! – WORRIED ED

YOU DON'T MIND IF I BORROW ONE OF YOUR **CANNONS**, DO YOU?

OH, I SAY!

AND I'LL NEED THIS TOO!

OI! KEEP OFF THE GRASS!

WAHEY! INTRODUCING THE **WORLD'S BIGGEST WATER PISTOL!**

PLUS THE RECORD FOR THE MOST PEOPLE SOAKED IN ONE SECOND GOES TO... **ME!**

RIGHT! TIME FOR THE NEXT RECORD! MUM, I NEED TO BORROW YOUR MAKE-UP!

YOU **WANT** TO WEAR MAKE-UP?

BY THE WAY, WHY HAVE WE RECEIVED A POSTCARD FROM YOUR FATHER?

BYE!

NEED TO MAKE MYSELF LOOK JUST PERFECT...

TO SCARE KATE SILLY!

EEEEEEEEEEEEEEEEEEEEEEEEEEEEEEEEK!

WHOOP! LOUDEST **SCREAM** IN THE WORLD! ANOTHER RECORD BROKEN!

BUT, NEARBY...

ERK! WHAT'S THAT NOISE?

DANDYTOWN STINK BOMB CO.

SWERVE!

CRASH!!

SMASH!

AND ANOTHER! MOST STINK BOMBS **BROKEN** AT ONCE!

AND MOST PEOPLE, ERM... WELL, YOU KNOW! GULP!

HURL!

BLOIK!

GAG!

I'VE BROKEN TWO MORE RECORDS, AT LEAST.

MOST FUN I'VE EVER HAD IN ONE DAY!

AND BEING **CHASED** BY THE MOST PEOPLE EVER! GULP!

COME BACK HERE!

BRASSNECK!

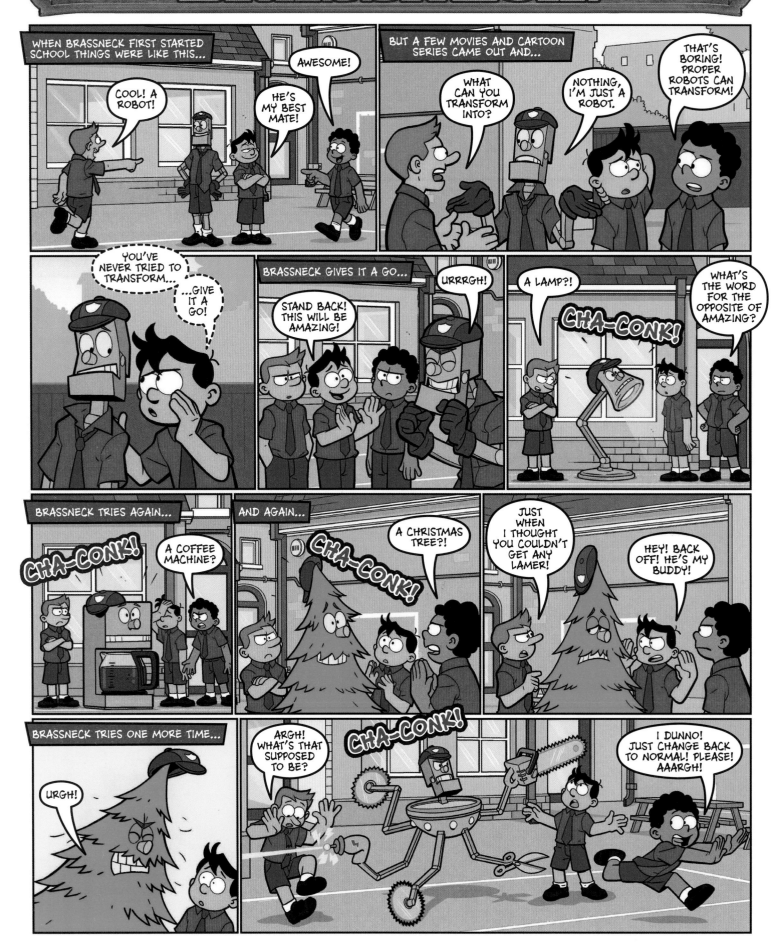

99: MY DAD'S A
100: DOOFUS

THE WORST MARK IN CLASS! AGAIN! HONESTLY, A **PIG** COULD DO BETTER THAN YOU!

NEXT DAY...

PSST! IT'S MULTIPLE CHOICE THIS TIME, DAD. YOU SHOULD FIND IT EASIER...

WEEEEEECKK!

AUGH!!

DON'T BE ALARMED, SON. I TAPED A PEN TO THIS PIG'S TROTTER AND SAT HIM IN MY PLACE!

HE HAS AS MUCH CHANCE OF GETTING THE ANSWERS RIGHT AS ME.

MEANWHILE, I CAN BUNK OFF AND SPEND THE DAY PLAYING FOOTY!

OI! OI!

DOOF!

AFTER THE TEST...

88 OUT OF 100! REMARKABLE, YOU'VE REALLY IMPROVED!

WHAT?

THAT'S INCREDIBLE! YOU'RE THE SMARTEST PIG IN THE WORLD!

GIVE ME THAT!

WEEEEECK!

GIVE ME IT! YOU'RE ONLY **PRETENDING** TO BE ME!

STR. EEEE-TCH!

WEEECK!

WE AGREE'D CARROTS!

NEW COMIC!

MY PIG'S A GENIIUS!!

OW! GERROFF! YOU'VE TORN IT!

CHOMP!

HA-HA-HA-HA!

JAMIE